VALERIE GREELEY'S

NATURE
ALPHABET
— *of* —
VERSE

Blackie

APPLES

APPLES
by Laurie Lee, b. 1914

Behold the apples' rounded worlds:
juice-green of July rain,
the black polestar of flower, the rind
mapped with its crimson stain.

The russet, crab and cottage red
burn to the sun's hot brass,
then drop like sweat from every branch
and bubble in the grass.

They lie as wanton as they fall,
and where they fall and break,
the stallion clamps his crunching jaws,
the starling stabs his beak.

In each plump gourd the cidery bite
of boys' teeth tears the skin;
the waltzing wasp consumes his share,
the bent worm enters in.

I, with as easy hunger, take
entire my season's dole;
welcome the ripe, the sweet, the sour,
the hollow and the whole.

BARN OWL

THE OWL
by Edward Thomas, 1878-1917

Downhill I came, hungry, and yet not starved;
Cold, yet had heat within me that was proof
Against the North wind; tired, yet so that rest
Had seemed the sweetest thing under a roof.

Then at the inn I had food, fire, and rest,
Knowing how hungry, cold, and tired was I.
All of the night was quite barred out except
An owl's cry, a most melancholy cry

Shaken out long and clear upon the hill,
No merry note, nor cause of merriment,
But one telling me plain what I escaped
And others could not, that night, as in I went.

And salted was my food, and my repose,
Salted and sobered, too, by the bird's voice
Speaking for all who lay under the stars,
Soldiers and poor, unable to rejoice.

CAT

TO MRS REYNOLDS'S CAT
by John Keats, 1795-1821

Cat! who hast passed thy grand climacteric,
  How many mice and rats hast in thy days
  Destroyed? How many tit-bits stolen? Gaze
With those bright languid segments green, and prick
Those velvet ears - but prithee do not stick
  Thy latent talons in me, and up-raise
  Thy gentle mew, and tell me all thy frays
Of fish and mice, and rats and tender chick.
Nay, look not down, nor lick thy dainty wrists -
  For all the wheezy asthma, and for all
Thy tail's tip is nicked off, and though the fists
  Of many a maid have given thee many a maul,
Still is that fur as soft as when the lists
  In youth thou enteredst on glass-bottled wall.

DUCKLINGS

FOUR DUCKS ON A POND

by William Allingham, 1824-89

Four ducks on a pond,
A grass-bank beyond,
A blue sky of spring,
White clouds on the wing;
What a little thing
To remember for years -
To remember with tears!

EAGLE

THE EAGLE
by Alfred, Lord Tennyson, 1809-92

He clasps the crag with crooked hands;
Close to the sun in lonely lands,
Ring'd with the azure world, he stands.

The wrinkled sea beneath him crawls;
He watches from his mountain walls.
And like a thunderbolt he falls.

FOX

THE VIXEN
by John Clare, 1793-1864

Among the taller wood with ivy hung,
The old fox plays and dances round her young.
She snuffs and barks if any passes by
And swings her tail and turns prepared to fly.
The horseman hurries by, she bolts to see,
And turns agen, from danger never free.
If any stands she runs among the poles
And barks and snaps and rives them in the holes.
The shepherd sees them and the boy goes by
And gets a stick and progs the hole to try.
They get all still and lie in safety sure,
And out again when everything's secure,
And start and snap at blackbirds bouncing by
To fight and catch the great white butterfly.

GERMANDER SPEEDWELL AND GROUNDSEL

HEAVEN IN A
WILD FLOWER
by William Blake, 1757-1827

To see a world in a grain of sand,
And a Heaven in a wild flower,
Hold infinity in the palm of your hand,
And Eternity in an hour.

HEDGEHOG

THE HEDGEHOG
by John Clare, 1793-1864
(Extract)

The hedgehog hides beneath the rotten hedge
And makes a great round nest of grass and sedge
Or in a bush or in a hollow tree
And many often stoop and say they see
Him roll and fill his prickles full of crabs
And creep away and where the magpie dabs
His wing at muddy dyke in aged root
He makes a nest and fills it full of fruit
On the hedge-bottom hunts for crabs and sloes
And whistles like a cricket as he goes.

IVY

SONG
by Christina Rossetti, 1830-94

Oh roses for the flush of youth,
  And laurel for the perfect prime;
But pluck an ivy branch for me
  Grown old before my time.

Oh violets for the grave of youth,
  And bay for those dead in their prime;
Give me the withered leaves I chose
  Before in the old time.

JACOB'S LADDER AND JACK-GO-TO-BED-AT-NOON

COCK-A-CLAY
by John Clare, 1793-1864

In the cowslip's peeps I lye
Hidden from the buzzing fly
While green grass beneath me lies
Pearled wi' dew like fishes' eyes
Here I lie a Cock-a-Clay
Waiting for the time o'day

While grassy forests quake surprise
And the wild wind sobs and sighs
My gold home rocks as like to fall
On its pillar green and tall
When the pattering rain drives by
Clock-a-Clay keeps warm and dry

Day by day and night by night
All the week I hide from sight
In the cowslip's peeps I lie
In rain and dew still warm and dry
Day and night and night and day
Red black-spotted Cock-a-Clay

My home it shakes in wind and showers
Pale green pillar topt wi'flowers
Bending at the wild wind's breath
Till I touch the grass, beneath
Here still I live lone Cock-a-Clay
Watching for the time of day

KINGFISHER

THE KINGFISHER
by William Henry Davies, 1871-1940

It was the Rainbow gave thee birth,
  And left thee all her lovely hues;
And, as her mother's name was Tears,
  So runs it in thy blood to choose
For haunts the lonely pools, and keep
In company with trees that weep.

Go you and, with such glorious hues,
  Live with proud Peacocks in green parks;
On lawns as smooth as shining glass,
  Let every feather show its marks;
Get thee on boughs and clap thy wings
Before the windows of proud kings.

Nay, lovely Bird, thou art not vain;
  Thou hast no proud, ambitious mind,
I also love a quiet place
  That's green, away from all mankind;
A lonely pool, and let a tree
Sigh with her bosom over me.

LITTLE OWL

WINTER
by William Shakespeare, 1564-1616

When icicles hang by the wall
  And Dick the shepherd blows his nail,
And Tom bears logs into the hall,
  And milk comes frozen home in pail;
When blood is nipt, and ways be foul,
Then nightly sings the staring owl
                    Tuwhoo!
Tuwhit! tuwhoo! A merry note!
While greasy Joan doth keel the pot.

When all around the wind doth blow,
  And coughing drowns the parson's saw,
And birds sit brooding in the snow,
  And Marian's nose looks red and raw;
When roasted crabs hiss in the bowl -
Then nightly sings the staring owl
                    Tuwhoo!
Tuwhit! tuwhoo! A merry note!
While greasy Joan doth keel the pot.

MUSHROOMS

MUSHROOM
by Emily Dickinson, 1830-86

The Mushroom is the Elf of Plants -
At Evening, it is not -
At Morning, in a Truffled Hut
It stops upon a Spot

As if it tarried always
And yet its whole Career
Is shorter than a Snake's Delay
And fleeter than a Tare -

'Tis Vegetation's Juggler -
The Germ of Alibi -
Doth like a Bubble antedate
And like a Bubble, hie -

I feel as if the Grass was pleased
To have it intermit -
This surreptitious scion
Of Summer's circumspect.

Had Nature any supple Face
Or could she one contemn -
Had Nature an Apostate -
That Mushroom - it is Him!

NEST

NIGHT
by William Blake, 1757-1827
(Extract)

The sun descending in the west
The evening star does shine,
The birds are silent in their nest
And I must seek for mine,
The moon, like a flower
In heaven's high bower,
With silent delight
Sits and smiles on the night.

Ox-eye Daisies and Orange-tip Butterfly

THE WILD FLOWER'S SONG

by William Blake, 1757-1827

As I wander'd the forest
The green leaves among,
I heard a wild flower
Singing a song:

'I slept in the Earth
In the silent night;
I murmur'd my fears
And I felt delight.

'In the morning I went
As rosy as morn
To seek for new Joy,
But O! met with scorn.'

PEACOCK BUTTERFLY

I Meant to Do
My Work Today

by Richard le Gallienne, 1866-1947

I meant to do my work today
But a brown bird sang in the apple tree,
And a butterfly flitted across the field,
And all the leaves were calling me.

And the wind went sighing over the land,
Tossing the grasses to and fro,
And a rainbow held out its shining hand -
So what could I do but laugh and go?

QUAKING GRASS AND QUEEN OF SPAIN FRITILLARY

THE GRASS SO LITTLE HAS TO DO

by Emily Dickinson, 1830-86

The Grass so little has to do -
A Sphere of simple Green -
With only Butterflies to brood
And Bees to entertain -

And stir all day to pretty Tunes
The Breezes fetch along -
And hold the Sunshine in its lap
And bow to everything -

And thread the Dews, all night, like Pearls -
And make itself so fine
A Duchess were too common
For such a noticing -

And even when it dies - to pass
In Odors so divine -
Like Lowly spices, lain to sleep -
Or Spikenards, perishing -

And then, in Sovereign Barns to dwell -
And dream the Days away,
The Grass so little has to do
I wish I were a Hay -

RABBIT

SONG OF THE RABBITS OUTSIDE THE TAVERN

by Elizabeth Coatsworth, 1893-1986

We who play under the pines,
We who dance in the snow
That shines blue in the light of the moon
Sometimes halt as we go,
Stand with our ears erect,
Our noses testing the air,
To gaze at the golden world
Behind the windows there.

Suns they have in a cave
And stars each on a tall white stem,
And the thought of fox or night owl
Seems never to trouble them,
They laugh and eat and are warm,
Their food seems ready at hand,
While hungry out in the cold
We little rabbits stand.

But they never dance as we dance,
They have not the speed nor the grace.
We scorn both the cat and the dog
Who lie by their fireplace.
We scorn them licking their paws,
Their eyes on an upraised spoon,
We who dance hungry and wild
Under a winter's moon.

SQUIRREL

SQUIRRELS
by John Mole, b. 1941

Tails like dandelion clocks
They blow away, these
Light-weight bucking broncos
With a plume behind.

For sheer surprise
No well-aimed burdock
Sticks more nimbly to your overcoat
Than these to tree bark,

Nor with such aplomb
Can any comparable creature
Lead a dance more deftly
Through the branches.

Down to earth again, they
Hold their tums in, little aldermen,
Or sit on tree stumps
Like old ladies knitting socks.

TOADS AND TOADSTOOLS

EVENING
by Percy Bysshe Shelley, 1792-1822

The sun is set; the swallows are asleep;
The bats are flitting fast in the grey air;
The slow soft toads out of damp corners creep,
And evening's breath, wandering here and there
Over the quivering surface of the stream,
Wakes not one ripple from its summer dream.

UPRIGHT YELLOW SORREL AND VIOLETS

MARCH VIOLETS
by John Clare, 1793-1864

Where last year's leaves and weeds decay
March violets are in blow
I'd rake the rubbish all away
And give them room to grow

Near neighbours to the Arum proud
Where dew-drops fall and sleep
As purple as a fallen cloud
March violets bloom and creep

Scenting the gales of early morn
They smell before they're seen
Peeping beneath the old whitethorn
That shows its tender green

The lamb will nibble by their bloom
And eat them day by day
Till briars forbid his steps to come
And then he skips away

'Mid nettle stalks that wither there
And on the greensward lie
All bleaching in the thin March air
The scattered violets lie.

WOOD MOUSE

TO A FIELD MOUSE
by Robert Burns, 1759-96
(Extract)

Wee, sleekit, cow'rin', tim'rous beastie,
O what a panic's in thy breastie!
Thou need na start awa sae hasty,
Wi' bickering brattle!
I wad be laith to rin an' chase thee
Wi' murd'ring pattle!

I'm truly sorry man's dominion
Has broken nature's social union,
An' justifies that ill opinion
Which makes thee startle
At me, thy poor earth-born companion,
An fellow-mortal!

YELLOW VETCH AND ZIG-ZAG CLOVER

OF CLOVERS
AND OF NOON
by Emily Dickinson, 1830-86

His Feet are shod with Gauze -
His Helmet is of Gold,
His Breast, a Single Onyx
With Chrysophrase, inlaid.

His Labour is a Chant -
His Idleness - a Tune -
Oh, for a Bee's experience
Of Clovers, and of Noon!

Acknowledgments

The author and the publisher would like to thank the following for their kind permission to reprint copyright material in this book:

'Apples' from *Selected Poems* by Laurie Lee (Penguin Books, 1985, first published, 1983), copyright © Laurie Lee, 1983; 'I Meant to Do My Work Today' by Richard le Gallienne, reprinted by permission of the Society of Authors as the literary representative of the Estate of Richard le Gallienne; 'Song of the Rabbits Outside the Tavern' by Elizabeth Coatsworth reprinted with permission of Macmillan Publishing Company from *Away Goes Sally* by Elizabeth Coatsworth, copyright © 1934 by Macmillan Publishing Company, renewed 1962 by Elizabeth Coatsworth Beston; 'Squirrels' by John Mole, copyright John Mole, from *Boo to a Goose* (1987), reproduced by permission of Peterloo Poets.

Every effort has been made to trace the copyright holders, but the author and publisher apologize if any inadvertent omission has been made.

BLACKIE CHILDREN'S BOOKS

Published by the Penguin Group
Penguin Books Ltd, 27 Wrights Lane, London W8 5TZ, England
Penguin Books USA Inc., 375,Hudson Street, New York, New York 10014, USA
Penguin Books Australia Ltd, Ringwood, Victoria, Australia
Penguin Books Canada Ltd, 10 Alcorn Avenue, Toronto, Ontario, Canada M4V 3B2
Penguin Books (NZ) Ltd, 182-190 Wairau Road, Auckland 10, New Zealand

Penguin Books Ltd, Registered Offices: Harmondsworth, Middlesex, England

First published 1994
1 3 5 7 9 10 8 6 4 2
First edition

This selection copyright © Blackie Children's Books, 1994
Illustrations copyright © Valerie Greeley, 1994

The moral right of the illustrator has been asserted

Made and printed in Hong Kong

A CIP catalogue record for this book is available from the British Library

ISBN 0-216-94132-6